RO

HOOD

retold by Aaron Shepard and Anne L. Watson
illustrated by Jennifer Tanner

Librarian Reviewer
Allyson A.W. Lyga MS
Library Media/Graphic Novel Consultant

Reading Consultant
Mark DeYoung
Classroom Teacher

www.raintreepublishers.co.uk
Visit our website to find out
more information about
Raintree books.

To order:
☎ Phone +44 (0) 1865 888066
🖹 Fax +44 (0) 1865 314091
💻 Visit www.raintreepublishers.co.uk

Raintree is an imprint of Capstone Global Library Limited, a company incorporated in
England and Wales having its registered office at 7 Pilgrim Street, London, EC4V 6LB –
Registered company number: 6695582

"Raintree" is a registered trademark of Pearson Education Limited, under licence to
Capstone Global Library Limited

Text © Stone Arch Books, 2009
First published by Stone Arch Books in 2007
First published in hardback in the United Kingdom in 2009
First published in paperback in the United Kingdom in 2010
The moral rights of the proprietor have been asserted.

Art Director: Heather Kindseth
Graphic Designer: Kay Fraser
Edited in the UK by Laura Knowles
Printed and bound in China by Leo Paper Products Ltd

ISBN 978-1406212495 (hardback)
13 12 11 10 09
10 9 8 7 6 5 4 3 2 1

ISBN 978-1406213515 (paperback)
14 13 12 11 10
10 9 8 7 6 5 4 3 2 1

British Library Cataloguing in Publication Data
Shepard, Aaron.
Robin Hood. -- (Graphic revolve)
741.5-dc22
A full catalogue record for this book is available from the British Library.

Table of Contents

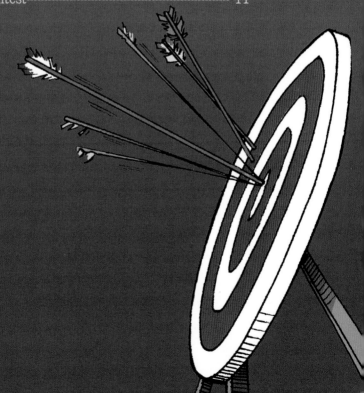

Introducing . . .

Robin Hood
A bold young outlaw

Marian
Robin's love

Will Scarlet
Robin's cousin

Little John
Robin's right-hand man

Edward and Sir Stephen
Eleanor's father and his chosen groom

Eleanor and Alan-a-Dale
A wandering minstrel and his love

Friar Tuck
A wandering monk

David of Doncaster and Will Stutely
Other men of Robin's band

Sheriff of Nottingham
A nobleman who carries out
the law and collects taxes

Bishop of Hereford
A man of the Church

King Richard
Ruler of England from 1189 to 1199

19

23

Would Eleanor marry you against her father's wishes?

Yes!

I know a friar with no love of the rich and mighty.

Just through those trees is where you'll find Friar Tuck.

29

31

35

So a great feast is served to the sounds of laughter and Alan-a-Dale's harp.

Then come the games.

RKRACK!

How do you like the entertainment, Sheriff?

Robin himself takes a turn at the bow.

41

45

The Sheriff's men are everywhere.

Be ready for a hasty retreat.

Robin, be careful.

Good luck, my love.

49

50

Most of the archers do well.

But only four qualify
for the second round.

55

About Robin Hood

The stories of Robin Hood's adventures were first told hundreds of years ago. The earliest known written story, *The Gest of Robin Hood*, was written around 1500.

The word "gest" means deed. This early version includes Maid Marian, Little John, and the Sheriff of Nottingham. In the 1800s, Howard Pyle, an American illustrator and writer, loved reading about Robin Hood. He retold these popular stories in 1883, in his book *The Merry Adventures of Robin Hood*.

About the Authors

Aaron Shepard and Anne L. Watson are a husband and wife writing team. Aaron is the award-winning author of many retellings of folktales and world classics for young readers. His books include *The Legend of Lightning Larry* and *The Sea King's Daughter*. Anne is a novelist and photographer. They live in Washington, USA.

About the Illustrator

When she was young, Jennifer Tanner loved to draw humorous comics about dogs who went on spectacular adventures through time and space, meeting alien creatures along the way. She's never lost that love for telling stories with pictures. She attended the Savannah College of Art and Design in the USA where she received her degree in Sequential Art. Today she spends her time illustrating many comic books.

Glossary

abbey (AB-ee) – place where religious men and women live

archery (AR-chuh-ree) – a sport using a bow and arrows to hit a target

bishop (BISH-up) – the leader for churches in an area; the priests in the different churches report to the bishop

friar (FRY-ur) – a man whose job is to serve God and the church; monk is another name for a friar

groom (GROOM) – a man who is about to get married or was just married

minstrel (MIN-strul) – a person who works as a singer or plays a musical instrument

outlaw (OUT-law) – a person who disobeys the law and is in hiding

staff (STAF) – a stick or cane used for walking

starving (STARV-ing) – dying because of a lack of food

tithe (TYTH) – part of a family's income or crop that the church collected to support its priests and bishops

Background of Robin Hood

Sherwood Forest, the setting for the tale of Robin Hood, is a forest that still exists in England. The forest today, however, is a much different place than it was in the late 1100s. Then, the forest belonged to the king of England. Only he and other noblemen were allowed to hunt there.

The sheriffs, friars, and bishops collected taxes and tithes from the people who lived in the communities near Sherwood Forest. Most of these people were poor farmers who worked hard to feed their families. These people relied on the goods of the forest — from the wood for heat and shelter to the plants and wildlife for food. Many people hunted illegally to provide their families with food, even though they could be hanged for breaking the law. Those who were in trouble with the law, like Robin Hood, often hid deep in the forest.

The story of Robin Hood, whether it was true or not, gave people hope that such an unfair way of living would come to an end.

N

W   E

S

SCOTLAND

Sherwood Forest

Nottingham

ENGLAND

WALES

London

English
Channel

Atlantic Ocean

ROBIN HOOD'S ENGLAND
1193 CE

Discussion Questions

1. Why did Robin Hood steal from the rich and give to the poor? Do you think that was fair? Why or why not?

2. Why did people join Robin Hood's band of thieves?

3. What if there were a person today who lived like Robin Hood, robbing rich people and giving the money to poor people. Would he be wanted by the police? Would his face be on the TV news? Would you want to join his band? Explain.

Writing Prompts

1. Instead of robbing from the rich, make a list of things you can actually do to help the poor in your community.

2. Robin Hood was very good at archery. Describe a sport or activity that you do well.

3. King Richard ruled over a kingdom that had very rich and very poor people living in it. If you were the king or queen of a country like his, what would you do to make life more fair for everyone? Do you have ideas about how to be a good ruler?

Other Books

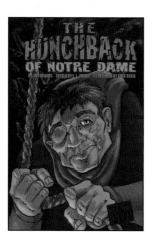

**THE HUNCHBACK OF
NOTRE DAME**

Hidden away in the bell tower of the
Cathedral of Notre Dame, Quasimodo
is treated like a beast. Although he is
gentle and kind, he has the reputation
of a frightening monster because of
his physical deformities. He develops
affection for Esmeralda, a gypsy girl
who shows him kindness in return.
When the girl is sentenced to an
unfair death by hanging, Quasimodo
is determined to save her. But those
closest to Quasimodo have other plans
for the gypsy.

GULLIVER'S TRAVELS

Lemuel Gulliver always dreamed
of sailing across seas, but he never
could have imagined the places his
travels would take him. On the island
of Lilliput, he is captured by tiny
creatures no more than six inches tall.
In a country of Blefuscu, he is nearly
squashed by an army of giants. His
adventures could be the greatest tales
ever told, if he survives long enough
to tell them.

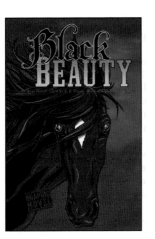

BLACK BEAUTY

Black Beauty, a handsome colt living in Victorian England, had a happy childhood growing up in the peaceful countryside. In his later years, he encounters terrible illness and a frightening stable fire. Things go from bad to worse when Black Beauty's new owners begin renting him out for profit. Black Beauty endures a life of mistreatment and disrespect in a world that shows little regard for the wellbeing of animals.

TREASURE ISLAND

Jim Hawkins had no idea what he was getting into when the pirate Billy Bones showed up at the doorstep of his mother's inn. When Billy dies suddenly, Jim is left to unlock his old sea chest, which reveals money, a journal, and a treasure map. Joined by a band of honourable men, Jim sets sail on a dangerous voyage to locate the loot on a faraway island. The violent sea is only one of the dangers they face. They soon encounter a band of bloodthirsty pirates determined to make the treasure their own!

Graphic Revolve

If you have enjoyed this story, there are many more exciting tales for you to discover in the Graphic Revolve collection...

20,000 Leagues Under the Sea

Black Beauty

Dracula

Frankenstein

Gulliver's Travels

The Hound of the Baskervilles

The Hunchback of Notre Dame

King Arthur and the Knights of the Round Table

Robin Hood

The Strange Case of Dr Jekyll and Mr Hyde

Treasure Island

The War of the Worlds